P9-DCP-651

SGT. PEPPER'S LONELY HEARTS CLUB BAND

THE BEATLES

Contents

This publication is not for sale in
the E.C. and/or Australia
or New Zealand.

Ray's Music
21 W. Front St., (313) - 242-7244
MONROE, MI 48161-2393

HAL•LEONARD™
CORPORATION

7777 W. BLUEMOUND RD. P.O. BOX 13819 MILWAUKEE, WI 53213

The location: Chelsea Manor Studios, Flood Street, London.
The date: Thursday, March 30, 1967. The crowd assembled...

1 Sri Yukteswar Giri (guru)
2 Aleister Crowley (dabbler in sex, drugs and magic)
3 Mae West (actress) 4 Lenny Bruce (comic)
5 Karlheinz Stockhausen (composer)
6 W.C. (William Claude) Fields (comic)
7 Carl Gustav Jung (psychologist)
8 Edgar Allen Poe (writer) 9 Fred Astaire (actor)
10 Richard Merkin (artist)
11 The Varga Girl (by artist Alberto Vargas)
*12 Leo Gorcey (actor)
13 Huntz hall (actor, with Leo Gorcey,
    one of the Bowery Boys)
14 Simon Rodia (creator of Watts Towers)
15 Bob Dylan (musician)
16 Aubrey Beardsley (illustrator)
17 Sir Robert Peel
18 Aldous Huxley (writer) 19 Dylan Thomas (poet)
20 Terry Southern (writer) 21 Dion (di Mucci) (singer)
22 Tony Curtis (actor)
23 Wallace Berman (actor)
24 Tommy Handley (comic) 25 Marilyn Monroe (actress)
26 William Burroughs (writer)
27 Sri Mahavatara Babaji (guru)
28 Stan Laurel (comic) 29 Richard Lindner (artist)
30 Oliver Hardy (comic)
31 Karl Marx (philosopher/socialist)
32 H.G. (Herbert George) Wells (writer)
33 Sri Paramahansa Yagananda (guru)
34 Anonymous (wax hairdressers' dummy)
35 Stuart Sutcliffe (artist/former Beatle)
36 Anonymous (wax hairdressers' dummy)
37 Max Miller (comic)
38 The Petty Girl (by artist George Petty)
39 Marlon Brando (actor) 40 Tom Mix (actor)
41 Oscar Wilde (writer)
42 Tyrone Power (actor)
43 Larry Bell (artist)
44 Dr. David Livingstone (missionary/explorer)
45 Johnny Weismuller (swimmer/actor)
46 Stephen Crane (writer)
47 Issy Bonn (comic)
48 George Bernard Shaw (writer)
49 H.C. (Horace Clifford) Westermann (sculptor)
50 Albert Stubbins (soccer player)
51 Sri Lahiri Mahasaya (guru)
52 Lewis Carroll (writer)
53 T.E. (Thomas Edward) Lawrence (soldier,
    a/k/a Lawrence of Arabia)
54 Sonny Liston (boxer)
55 The Petty Girl (by artist George Petty)
56 Wax model of George Harrison
57 Wax model of John Lennon
58 Shirley Temple (child actress)
59 Wax model of Ringo Starr
60 Wax model of Paul McCartney
61 Albert Einstein (physicist)
62 John Lennon, holding a French horn
63 Ringo Starr, holding a trumpet
64 Paul McCartney, holding a cor anglais
65 George Harrison, holding a flute
66 Bobby Breen (singer)
67 Marlene Dietrich (actress)
#68 Mohandas Karamchand Ghandi (Indian leader)
69 Legionnaire from the Order of the Buffalos
70 Diana Dors (actress)
71 Shirley Temple (child actress)
72 Cloth grandmother-figure by Jann Haworth
73 Cloth figure of Shirley Temple (child actress)
    by Jann Haworth
74 Mexican candlestick
75 Television set
76 Stone figure of girl
77 Stone figure
§78 Statue from John Lennon's house
79 Trophy
80 Four-armed Indian doll
81 Drum-skin, designed by Joe Ephgrave
82 Hookah (water tobacco-pipe)
83 Velvet snake
84 Japanese stone figure
85 Stone figure of Snow White
86 Garden gnome
87 Tuba

* Painted out because he requested a fee
# Painted out at the request of EMI
§ Also used by Peter Blake as the basis
for the cut-out of Sgt. Pepper

The recording of *Sgt. Pepper's Lonely Hearts Club Band* spanned 129 days, perhaps the most creative 129 days in the history of rock music. Here, in the order in which the recordings were tackled, is a guide to the way the album was made.

'When I'm Sixty Four'. Recording commenced in studio two at Abbey Road on December 6, 1966. Album version mixed from take four. Writer: Paul. Lead vocal: Paul. Producer: George Martin. Recording engineer: Geoff Emerick. Second engineer: Phil McDonald.

'A Day In The Life'. Recording commenced in studio two at Abbey Road on January 19, 1967. Working title 'In The Life Of . . .'. Album version mixed from takes six and seven. Writers: John with Paul. Lead vocal: John, with Paul. Producer: George Martin. Recording engineer: Geoff Emerick. Second engineers: Richard Lush, Phil McDonald.

'Sgt. Pepper's Lonely Hearts Club Band'. Recording commenced in studio two at Abbey Road on February 1, 1967. Album version mixed from take ten. Writer: Paul. Lead vocal: Paul. Producer: George Martin. Recording engineer: Geoff Emerick. Second engineer: Richard Lush.

'Good Morning Good Morning'. Recording commenced in studio two at Abbey Road on February 8, 1967. Album version mixed from take eleven. Writer: John. Lead vocal: John. Producer: George Martin. Recording engineer: Geoff Emerick. Second engineer: Richard Lush.

'Being For The Benefit Of Mr. Kite!'. Recording commenced in studio two at Abbey Road on February 17, 1967. Album version mixed from take nine. Writer: John. Lead vocal: John. Producer: George Martin. Recording engineer: Geoff Emerick. Second engineer: Richard Lush.

'Fixing A Hole'. Recording commenced at Regent Sound Studio, Tottemham Court Road, London, on February 21, 1967, and later completed at Abbey Road. Album version mixed from take three. Writer: Paul. Lead vocal: Paul. Producer: George Martin. Recording engineers: Adrian Ibbetson (Regent Sound), Geoff Emerick (Abbey Road). Second engineer: Richard Lush.

'Lovely Rita'. Recording commenced in studio two at Abbey Road on February 23, 1967. Album version mixed from take eleven. Writer: Paul. Lead vocal: Paul. Producer: George Martin. Recording engineer: Geoff Emerick. Second engineer: Richard Lush.

'Lucy In The Sky With Diamonds'. Recording commenced in studio two at Abbey Road on March 1, 1967. Album version mixed from take eight. Writer: John. Lead vocal: John. Producer: George Martin. Recording engineer: Geoff Emerick. Second engineer: Richard Lush.

'Getting Better'. Recording commenced in studio two at Abbey Road on March 9, 1967. Album version mixed from take fifteen. Writer: Paul. Lead vocal: Paul. Producer: George Martin. Recording engineers: Malcolm Addey, Ken Townsend, Geoff Emerick, Peter Vince. Second engineers: Graham Kirkby, Richard Lush, Keith Slaughter.

'She's Leaving Home'. Recording commenced in studio two at Abbey Road on March 17, 1967. Album version mixed from take nine. Writer: Paul, with John. Lead vocal: Paul. Producer: George Martin. Score: Mike Leander. Recording engineer: Geoff Emerick. Second engineers: Richard Lush, Keith Slaughter.

'Within You Without You'. Recording commenced in studio two at Abbey Road on March 22, 1967. Album version mixed from take two. Writer: George. Lead vocal: George. Producer: George Martin. Recording engineer: Geoff Emerick. Second engineer: Richard Lush.

'With A Little Help From My Friends'. Recording commenced in studio two at Abbey Road on March 29, 1967. Working title 'Bad Finger Boogie'. Album version mixed from take eleven. Writers: John and Paul. Lead vocal: Ringo. Producer: George Martin. Recording engineer: Geoff Emerick. Second engineer: Richard Lush.

'Sgt. Pepper's Lonely Hearts Club Band (Reprise)'. Recording commenced in studio one at Abbey Road on April 1, 1967. Album version mixed from take nine. Writer: Paul. Lead vocal: John, Paul and George. Producer: George Martin. Recording engineer: Geoff Emerick. Second engineer: Richard Lush.

SGT. PEPPER'S LONELY HEARTS CLUB BAND

Moderately slow, but with a strong beat

Words and Music by
JOHN LENNON and PAUL McCARTNEY

WITH A LITTLE HELP FROM MY FRIENDS

Words and Music by JOHN LENNON
and PAUL McCARTNEY

What would you do___ if I sang___ out of tune?___ Would you stand___
What do I do___ when my love___ is a-way?___ (Does it wor-
(Would you be-lieve___ in a love___ at first sight?)___ Yes I'm cer-

___ up and walk___ out on me?___
-ry you to be a-___ lone?)___
-tain that it hap-pens all the time.

Lend me your ears___ and I'll sing___
How do I feel___ by the end___
(What do you see___ when you turn___

LUCY IN THE SKY WITH DIAMONDS

Words and Music by
JOHN LENNON and PAUL McCARTNEY

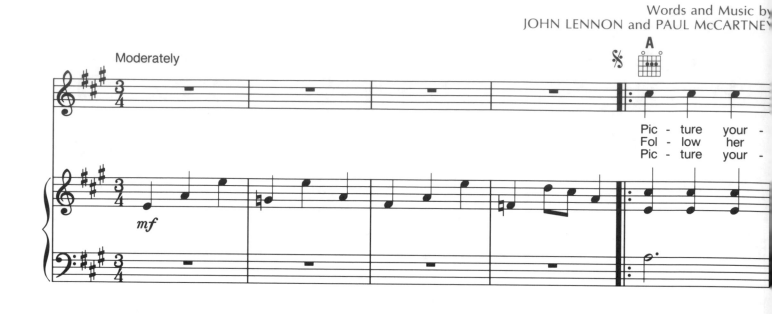

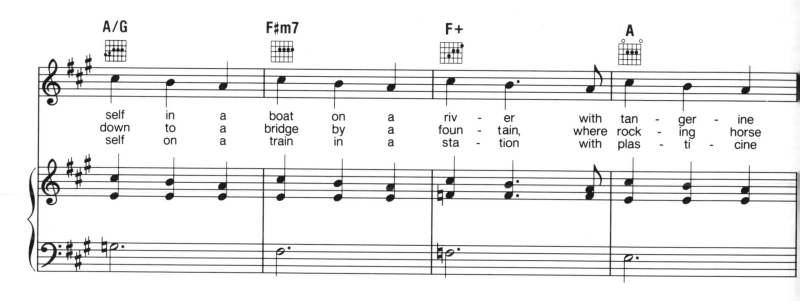

calls you, you an - swer quite slow - ly, a girl with ka -
smiles as you drift past the flow - ers that grow so in -
some - one is there at the turn - stile, the girl with ka -

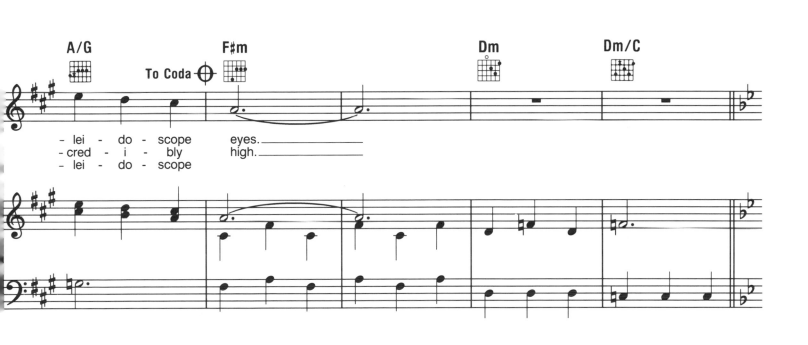

- lei - do - scope eyes.
- cred - i - bly high.
- lei - do - scope

Cel - lo - phane flow - ers of yel - low and green
News - pa - per tax - is ap - pear on the shore

GETTING BETTER

Words and Music by
JOHN LENNON and PAUL McCARTNEY

FIXING A HOLE

Words and Music by
JOHN LENNON and PAUL McCARTNEY

SHE'S LEAVING HOME

Words and Music by
JOHN LENNON and PAUL McCARTNEY

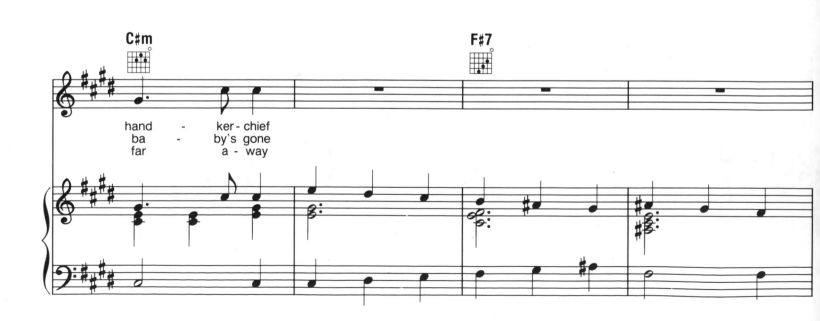

B11   **B9**

Qui - et - ly turn - ing the back - door key____
Why would she treat us so thought - less - ly____
Wait - ing to keep the ap - point - ment she made

B11   **B9**   **B7**

Step - ping out - side she is free
How could she do this to me
Meet - ing a man from the mo - tor trade

E

She_____ (We gave her most of our____ lives) is
She_____ (We nev - er thought of our____ selves) is
She_____ (What did we do that was____ wrong) is

30

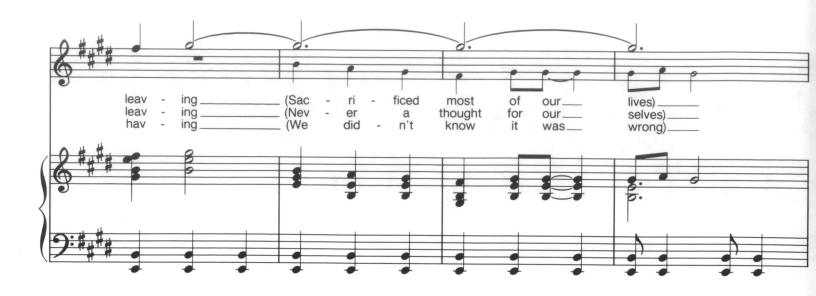

leav - ing _____ (Sac - ri - ficed most of our ___ lives) _____
leav - ing _____ (Nev - er a thought for our ___ selves) _____
hav - ing _____ (We did - n't know it was ___ wrong) _____

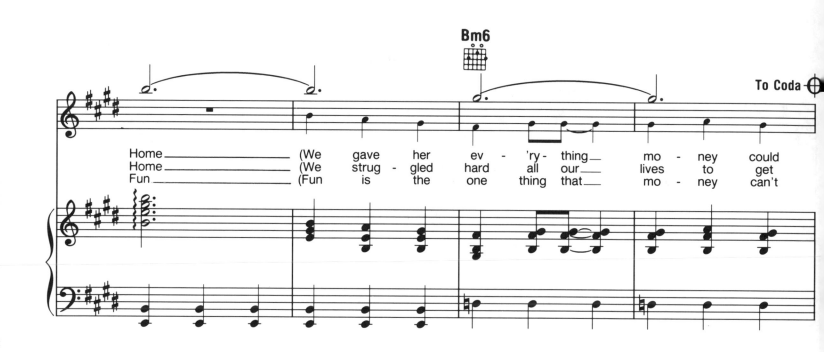

Home _____ (We gave her ev - 'ry - thing ___ mo - ney could
Home _____ (We strug - gled hard all our ___ lives to get
Fun _____ (Fun is the one thing that ___ mo - ney can't

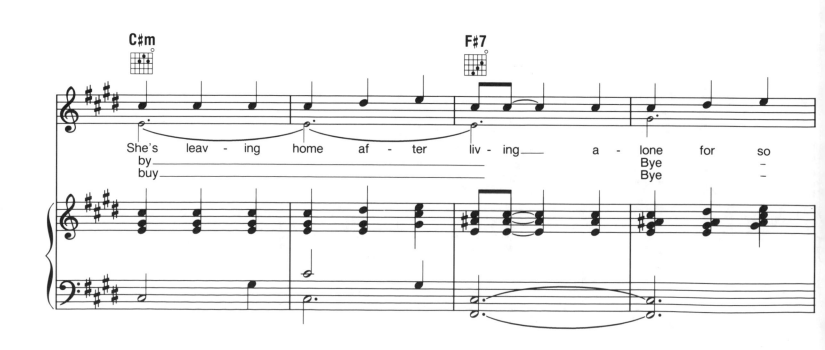

She's leav - ing home af - ter liv - ing ___ a - lone for so
by _____ Bye –
buy _____ Bye –

BEING FOR THE BENEFIT OF MR. KITE

Words and Music by JOHN LENNON and PAUL McCARTNEY

Original tempo

D.S. al Coda

The

WITHIN YOU WITHOUT YOU

Words and Music by
GEORGE HARRISON

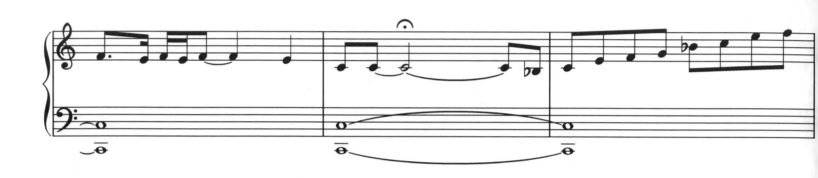

Moderately (strict tempo)

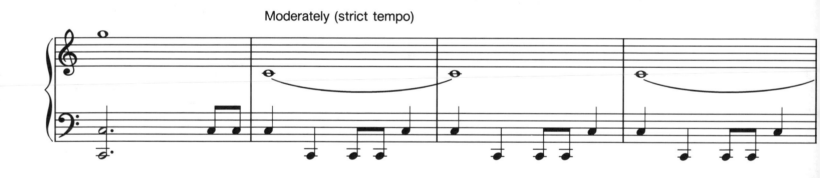

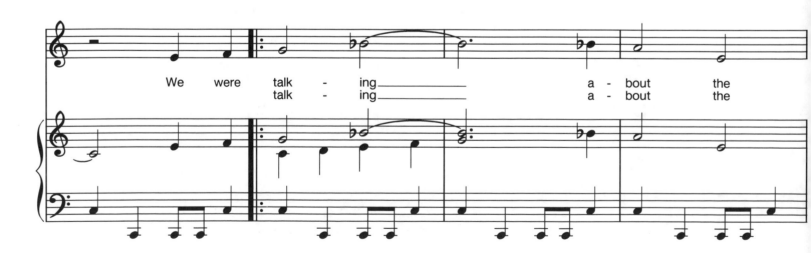

We were talk - ing _____ a - bout the
talk - ing _____ a - bout the

way.

We were love, with our love___ we could save the

world.   If they on - ly knew.___

Slightly faster

Try to re - a - lize it's all with - in your - self, no
And to see you're real - ly on - ly ver - y small, and

one else can make you change.

life flows on with - in you and with - out you.

With movement

Moderately (strict tempo)

We were talk - ing_____ a -

bout   the   love   that's   gone   so   cold,   And   the

peo - ple_____ who gain the world and

lose their soul. They don't know,_____ they can't

see._____ Are you one of them?

When you've seen be - yond your - self, then you may find peace
And the time will come when you see we're all one, peace and

of mind is wait - ing there.

life flows on with - in you and with - out you.

WHEN I'M SIXTY FOUR

Words and Music by
JOHN LENNON and PAUL McCARTNEY

Moderately

LOVELY RITA

Words and Music by
JOHN LENNON and PAUL McCARTNEY

me - ter   maid.

GOOD MORNING GOOD MORNING

Words and Music by JOHN LENNON
and PAUL McCARTNEY

Good morn - ing,— good morn - ing,— good morn - ing,— good morn - ing,— good morn - ing a.

Noth - ing to do— to save his life,— call his wife in.
Af - ter a while— you start to smile, now you feel cool.
Some - bod - y needs— to know the time, glad that I'm here.

Nothing to say___ but, "What a day!___ How's your boy
Then you decide___ to take a walk___ by the old
Watching the skirts,___ you start to flirt,___ now you're in

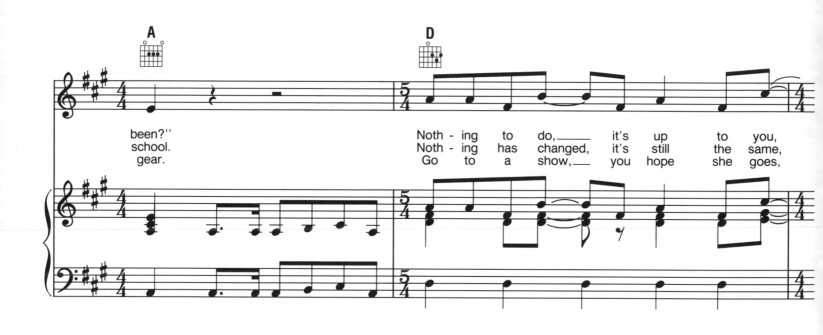

been?"
school.
gear.

Nothing to do,___ it's up to you,
Nothing has changed, it's still the same,
Go to a show,___ you hope she goes,

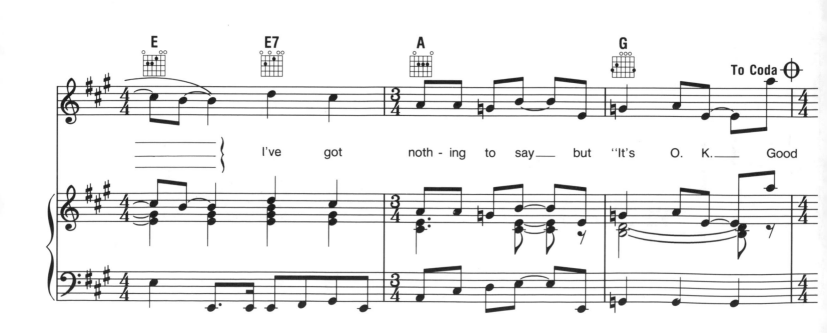

I've got nothing to say___ but "It's O.K.___ Good

morn - ing,__ good morn - ing,__ good morn - ing - a."

Go - ing to work,__ don't want to go,__ feel - ing low down,

Head - ing for home,__ you start to roam,___ then you're in

town.   Ev - 'ry - bod - y knows___ there's noth - ing do

ing, Ev- 'ry- thing is closed,__ it's like a ru - in, Ev - 'ry-one you see__ is half a-sleep__

__ and you're on your own,__ you're in the street.__

A DAY IN THE LIFE

Words and Music by
JOHN LENNON and PAUL McCARTNEY

SGT. PEPPER'S LONELY HEARTS CLUB BAND
It was twenty years ago today,
Sgt. Pepper taught the band to play
They've been going in and out of style
But they're guaranteed to raise a smile.
So may I introduce to you
The act you've known for all these years,
Sgt. Pepper's Lonely Hearts Club Band
We're Sgt. Pepper's Lonely Hearts Club Band,
We hope you will enjoy the show,
We're Sgt. Pepper's Lonely Hearts Club Band,
Sit back and let the evening go.
Sgt. Pepper's lonely, Sgt. Pepper's lonely,
Sgt. Pepper's Lonely Hearts Club Band.
It's wonderful to be here, It's certainly a thrill.
You're such a lovely audience,
We'd like to take you home with us,
We'd love to take you home.
I don't really want to stop the show,
But I thought that you might like to know,
That the singer's going to sing a song,
And he wants you all to sing along.
So let me introduce to you
The one and only Billy Shears
And Sgt. Pepper's Lonely Hearts Club Band.

A LITTLE HELP FROM MY FRIENDS
A little help from my friends
What would you think if I sang out of tune,
Would you stand up and walk out on me.
Lend me your ears and I'll sing you a song,
And I'll try not to sing out of key.
I get by with a little help from my friends,
I get high with a little help from my friends.
Going to try with a little help from my friends.
What do I do when my love is away.
(Does it worry you to be alone)
How do I feel by the end of the day
(Are you sad because you're on your own)
No I get by with a little help from my friends,
Do you need anybody,
I need somebody to love.
Could it be anybody
I want somebody to love.
Would you believe in a love at first sight,
Yes I'm certain that it happens all the time.
What do you see when you turn out the light,
I can't tell you, but I know it's mine.
Oh I get by with a little help from my friends,
Do you need anybody,
I just need somebody to love.
Could it be anybody,
I want somebody to love.
I get by with a little help from my friends,
Yes I get by with a little help from my friends,
With a little help from my friends.

LUCY IN THE SKY WITH DIAMONDS
Picture yourself in a boat on a river,
With a tangerine trees and marmalade skies
Somebody calls you, you answer quite slowly,
A girl with kaleidoscope eyes.
Cellophane flowers of yellow and green,
Towering over your head.
Look for the girl with the sun in her eyes
And she's gone.
Lucy in the sky with diamonds,
Follow her down to a bridge by a fountain
Where rocking horse people eat marshmallow pies,
Everyone smiles as you drift past the flowers,
That grow so incredibly high.
Newspaper taxis appear on the shore,
Waiting to take you away.
Climb in the back with your head in the clouds,
And you're gone.
Lucy in the sky with diamonds,
Picture yourself on a train in a station,
With plasticine porters with looking glass ties,
Suddenly someone is there at the turnstile,
The girl with kaleidoscope eyes.

GETTING BETTER
It's getting better all the time
I used to get mad at my school
The teachers that taught me weren't cool
You're holding me down, turning me round
Filling me up with your rules.
I've got to admit it's getting better
A little better all the time
I have to admit it's getting better
It's getting better since you've been mine.
Me used to be angry young man
Me hiding me head in the sand
You gave me the word
I finally heard
I'm doing the best that I can.
I've got to admit it's getting better
I used to be cruel to my woman
I beat her and kept her apart from the things
that she loved
Man I was mean but I'm changing my scene
And I'm doing the best that I can.
I admit it's getting better
A little better all the time
Yes I admit it's getting better
It's getting better since you've been mine.

FIXING A HOLE
I'm fixing a hole where the rain gets in
And stops my mind from wandering
Where it will go
I'm filling the cracks that ran through the door
And kept my mind from wandering
Where it will go
And it really doesn't matter if I'm wrong
I'm right
Where I belong I'm right
Where I belong
See the people standing there who disagree and
never win
And wonder why they don't get in my door.
I'm painting my room in the colourful way
And when my mind is wandering
There I will go.
And it really doesn't matter if
I'm wrong I'm right
Where I belong I'm right
Where I belong.
Silly people run around they worry me
And never ask me why they don't get past
my door.
I'm taking the time for a number of things
That weren't important yesterday
And I still go.
I'm fixing a hole where the rain gets in
And stops my mind from wandering
Where it will go.

SHE LEAVING HOME

Wednesday morning at five o'clock as the
day begins
Silently closing her bedroom door
Leaving the note that she hoped would
say more
She goes downstairs to the kitchen clutching
her handkerchief
Quietly turning the backdoor key
Stepping outside she is free.
She (We gave her most of our lives)
is leaving (Sacrificed most of our lives)
home (We gave her everything money
could buy)
She's leaving home after living alone
For so many years. Bye, bye
Father snores as his wife gets into her
dressing gown
Picks up the letter that's lying there
Standing alone at the top of the stairs
She breaks down and cries to her husband
Daddy our baby's gone.
Why would she treat us so thoughtlessly
How could she do this to me.
She (We never thought of ourselves)
is leaving (Never a thought for ourselves)
home (We struggled hard all our lives to get by)
She's leaving home after living alone
For so many years. Bye, bye
Friday morning at nine o'clock she is far away
Waiting to keep the appointment she made
Meeting a man from the motor trade.
She (What did we do that was wrong)
is having (We didn't know it was wrong) fun
Fun is the one thing that money can't buy
Something inside that was always denied
For so many years. Bye, bye
She's leaving home bye bye

BEING FOR THE BENEFIT OF MR. KITE!

For the benefit of Mr. Kite
There will be a show tonight on trampoline
The Hendersons will all be there
Late of Pablo Fanques Fair—what a scene
Over men and horses hoops and garters
Lastly through a hogshead of real fire!
In this way Mr. K. will challenge the world!
The celebrated Mr. K.
Performs his feat on Saturday at Bishopsgate
The Hendersons will dance and sing
As Mr. Kite flies through the ring don't be late
Messrs. K. and H. assure the public
Their production will be second to none
And of course Henry The Horse dances the waltz!
The band begins at ten to six
When Mr. K. performs his tricks without a sound
And Mr. H. will demonstrate
Ten summersets he'll undertake on solid ground
Having been some days in preparation
A splendid time is guaranteed for all
And tonight Mr. Kite is topping the bill.

John Lennon & Paul McCartney

WITHIN YOU WITHOUT YOU

We were talking—about the space between us all
And the people—who hide themselves behind a
wall of illusion
Never glimpse the truth—then it's far too late—
when they pass away.
We were talking—about the love we all could
share—when we find it
To try our best to hold it there—with our love
With our love—we could save the world—if
they only knew.
Try to realise it's all within yourself no-one else
can make you change
And to see you're really only very small,
and life flows on within you and without you.
We were talking—about the love that's gone so
cold and the people,
Who gain the world and lose their soul—
they don't know—they can't see—are you one
of them?
When you've seen beyond yourself—then you
may find, peace of mind, is waiting there—
And the time will come when you see
we're all one, and life flows on within you and
without you.

George Harrison

WHEN I'M SIXTY FOUR

When I get older losing my hair,
Many years from now.
Will you still be sending me a Valentine
Birthday greetings bottle of wine.
If I'd been out till quarter to three
Would you lock the door,
Will you still need me, will you still feed me,
When I'm sixty four.
You'll be older too,
And if you say the word,
I could stay with you.
I could be handy, mending a fuse
When your lights have gone.
You can knit a sweater by the fireside
Sunday morning go for a ride,
Doing the garden, digging the weeds,
Who could ask for more.
Will you still need me, will you still feed me,
When I'm sixty four.
Every summer we can rent a cottage,
In the Isle of Wight, if it's not too dear
We shall scrimp and save
Grandchildren on your knee
Vera Chuck & Dave
Send me a postcard, drop me a line,
Stating point of view
Indicate precisely what you mean to say
Yours sincerely, wasting away
Give me your answer, fill in a form
Mine for evermore
Will you still need me, will you still feed me.
When I'm sixty four.

LOVELY RITA

Lovely Rita meter maid.
Lovely Rita meter maid.
Lovely Rita meter maid.
Nothing can come between us,
When it gets dark I tow your hear away.
Standing by a parking meter,
When I caught a glimpse of Rita,
Filling in a ticket in her little white book.
In a cap she looked much older,
And the bag across her shoulder
Made her look a little like a military man.
Lovely Rita meter maid,
May I inquire discreetly,
When are you free,
To take some tea with me.
Took her out and tried to win her,
Had a laugh and over dinner,
Told her I would really like to see her again,
Got the bill and Rita paid it,
Took her home I nearly made it,
Sitting on the sofa with a sister or two.
Oh, lovely Rita meter maid,
where would I be without you,
Give us a wink and make me think of you.

GOOD MORNING, GOOD MORNING

Nothing to do to save his life call his wife in
Nothing to say but what a day how's your
boy been
Nothing to do it's up to you
I've got nothing to say but it's O.K.
Good morning, good morning...
Going to work don't want to go feeling
low down
Heading for home you start to roam then you're
in town
Everybody knows there's nothing doing
Everything is closed it's like a ruin
Everyone you see is half asleep.
And you're on your own you're in the street.
Good morning, good morning...
After a while you start to smile now you feel cool.
Then you decide to take a walk by the
old school.
Nothing had changed it's still the same
I've got nothing to say but it's O.K.
Good morning, good morning...
People running round it's five o'clock.
Everywhere in town is getting dark.
Everyone you see is full of life.
It's time for tea and meet the wife.
Somebody needs to know the time, glad that
I'm here.
Watching the skirts you start to flirt now you're
in gear.
Go to a show you hope she goes.
I've got nothing to say but it's O.K.
Good morning, good morning...

SGT. PEPPER'S LONELY HEARTS CLUB BAND
(Reprise)
We're Sergeant Pepper's Lonely Hearts
Club Band
We hope you have enjoyed the show
Sergeant Pepper's Lonely Hearts Club Band
We're sorry but it's time to go.
Sergeant Pepper's lonely.
Sergeant Pepper's lonely.
Sergeant Pepper's lonely.
Sergeant Pepper's lonely.
Sergeant Pepper's Lonely Hearts Club Band
We'd like to thank you once again
Sergeant Pepper's one and only Lonely Hearts
Club Band
It's getting very near the end
Sergeant Pepper's lonely
Sergeant Pepper's lonely
Sergeant Pepper's Lonely Hearts Club Band.

A DAY IN THE LIFE

I read the news today oh boy
About a lucky man who made the grade
And though the news was rather sad
Well I just had to laugh
I saw the photograph.
He blew his mind out in a car
He didn't notice that the lights had changed
A crowd of people stood and stared
They'd seen his face before
Nobody was really sure
If he was from the House of Lords.
I saw a film today oh boy
The English Army had just won the war
A crowd of people turned away
But I just had to look
Having read the book.
I'd love to turn you on
Woke up, fell out of bed,
Dragged a comb across my head
Found my way downstairs and drank a cup,
And looking up I noticed I was late.
Found my coat and grabbed my hat
Made the bus in seconds flat
Found my way upstairs and had a smoke,
Somebody spoke and I went into a dream
I read the news today oh boy
Four thousand holes in Blackburn, Lancashire
And though the holes were rather small
They had to count them all
Now they know how many holes it takes to fill
the Albert Hall.
I'd love to turn you on

John Lennon & Paul McCartney